TRICKS
AND
TREATS

STICKER ACTIVITY BOOK

Have fun completing the activities
in this trick-or-treat book!

*

Where there is a missing sticker, you will see
an empty shape. Search the sticker pages
to find the missing sticker.

Then go to the back of the book
to press out and create some
amazing masks!

make
believe
ideas

Creepy coloring

Color the creepy creatures.

monster

cat

spider

jack-o'-lantern

alien

skull

Hide-and-seek

Search the scene. Circle the different monsters.

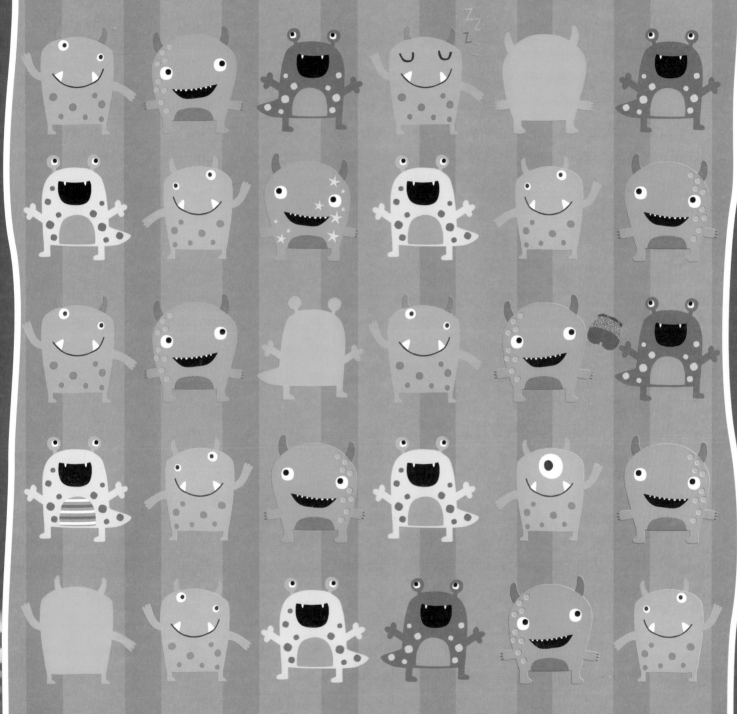

Who's asleep? Who has one eye? Who has stripes?

Who has a caramel apple? Who's covered in stars?

3

Find the difference

Circle five differences between the scenes.

4

Spooky owls

Find the owl that doesn't belong on each row.

Draw and color to finish the pictures.

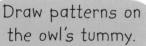
Draw patterns on the owl's tummy.

Fill the trick-or-treat bag with candy.

Mix and match

Draw lines from each monster to the matching colored candy.

purple candy

blue candy

pink monster

orange monster

pink candy

purple monster

blue monster

orange candy

Pumpkin patch

Use the key to color the picture.

Dot-to-dot

Connect the dots the see what
is carved on the jack-o'-lantern.

Trick or treat?

Circle the one that's different in each row.

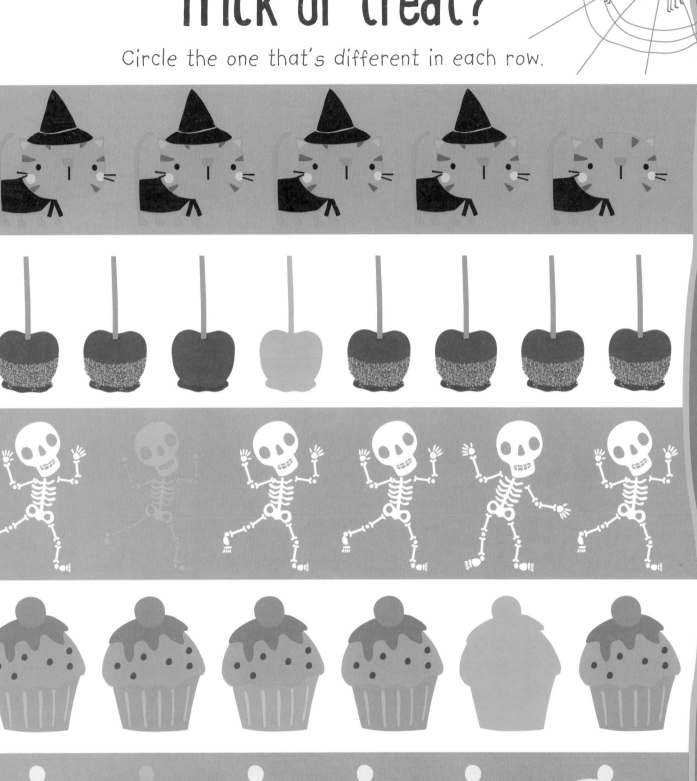

Bat maze

Guide the bats through the maze
to reach the haunted house.

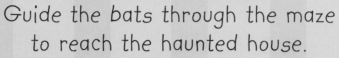

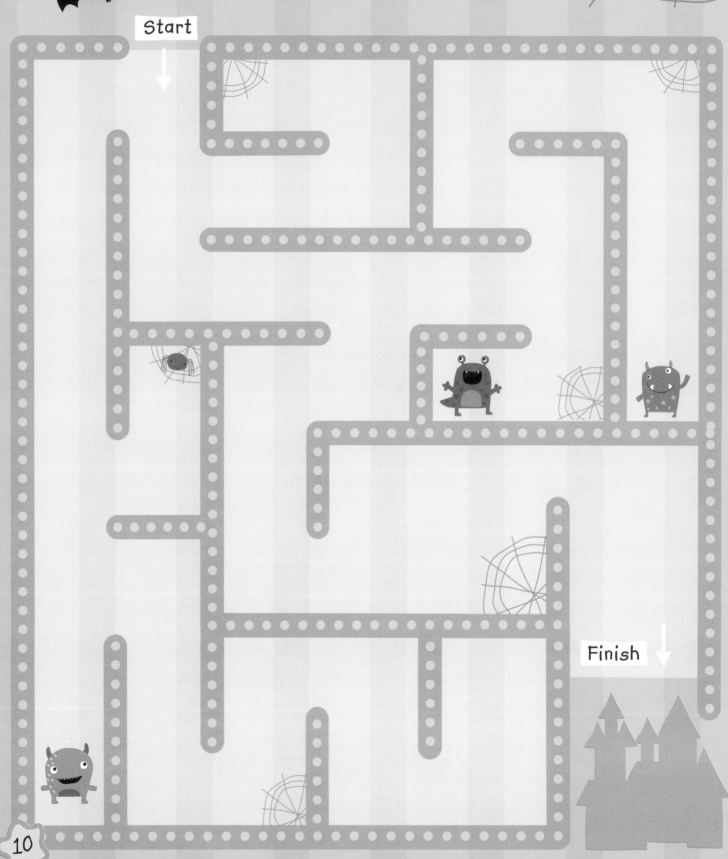

Start

Finish

Spooky sketches

Color the trick-or-treater and draw her
a friend in a fun Halloween costume.

Creepy coloring

Use color to finish the Halloween pictures.

owl

monster

trick-or-treat bag

caramel apples

pumpkin

bat

Hide-and-seek

Search the scene. Circle the different cats.

Who's wearing a hat? | Who's asleep? | Who has a kitten?

Who has found a mouse? | Who's wearing glasses?

Candy match

Count the treats. Draw lines from
each candy to the correct number.

Color by numbers

Use the key to color the picture.

1 **2** **3** **4** **5** **6** **7** **8** **9**

15

Amazing masks

1 Press out the mask shape, eye holes, and the small holes at either side.

2 Finish the mask using pencils, crayons, and stickers.

3 Ask an adult to thread some elastic or ribbon through the small holes and tie it around your head.